This Walker book
belongs to:

———————————

For Tom and Claire

First published 2008 by Walker Books Ltd
87 Vauxhall Walk, London SE11 5HJ

This edition published 2010

2 4 6 8 10 9 7 5 3 1

This book has been typeset in Gill Sans MT Schoolbook

Printed in China

British Library Cataloguing in Publication Data:
a catalogue record for this book is available
from the British Library

ISBN 978-1-4063-2550-8

www.walker.co.uk

Tilly and
her friends
all live
together in
a little yellow
house...

Hello
Tilly

Polly Dunbar

WALKER BOOKS
AND SUBSIDIARIES
LONDON • BOSTON • SYDNEY • AUCKLAND

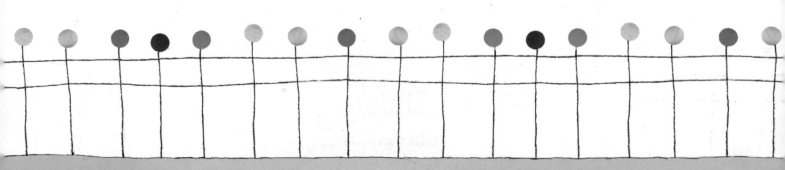

Tilly
was sitting
quietly.

She was
reading her
favourite
story.

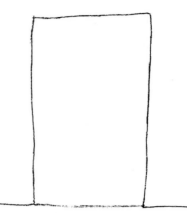

"Hello, Tilly,"
said Tiptoe.
"Will you play
with me?"

Tilly played her trumpet.

BOOM! BOOM! BOOM!

Tiptoe banged his drum.

BOOM! BOOM!

Hector
joined in.
He danced the
wiggly-woo!

"Quick!"

said Doodle.

"There's a feast!"

Mmmm...?

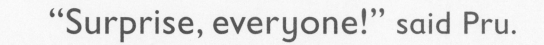

"Surprise, everyone!" said Pru.

"It's **ME!**"

"Don't I look

LOVELY!"

"We must all do the pretty-prance,"

said Pru. "Follow me!"

WHUMP!! BUMP! WHOOPS!

"Come
for
a ride!"

What a lot of fun!

BOOM! BOOM! BOOM!

Too much fun!

"Now
I think it's time
for a story,"
said Tilly.

"There were
six best friends,"
Tilly began,
"and they
all lived together
in a little
yellow house..."

The End

Polly Dunbar

Polly Dunbar is one of today's most exciting young author-illustrators, her warm and witty books captivating children the world over.

Polly based the Tilly and Friends stories on her own experience of sharing a house with friends. Tilly, Hector, Tumpty, Doodle, Tiptoe and Pru are all very different and they don't always get on. But in the little yellow house, full of love and laughter, no one can be sad or cross for long!

ISBN 978-1-4063-2550-8

ISBN 978-1-4063-2551-5

ISBN 978-1-4063-2614-7

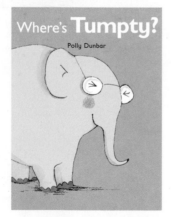

ISBN 978-1-4063-2613-0

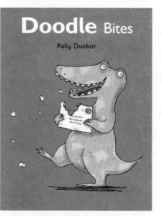

ISBN 978-1-4063-2615-4

ISBN 978-1-4063-2616-1

"Nobody can draw anything more instantly loveable than one of Dunbar's characters."
Independent on Sunday

Available from all good bookstores

www.walker.co.uk